50 Ways to please your lover

50 *Ways* to *please* your lover

hot sex tips to please your man

Cassandra Lorius

CICO BOOKS
LONDON NEW YORK

Published in 2010 by CICO Books
An imprint of Ryland Peters & Small Ltd
20–21 Jockey's Fields   519 Broadway, 5th Floor
London WC1R 4BW   New York, NY 10012

www.cicobooks.com

10 9 8 7 6 5 4 3 2 1

Text © Cassandra Lorius 2010
Design and illustrations © CICO Books 2010

A CIP catalog record for this book is available from the Library of Congress
and the British Library.

ISBN 978 1 906525 85 9

Printed in China

Design: David Fordham
Illustration: Trina Dalziel

THE BLACKBERRY BANG

PLAY THE FAME GAME

APPETITE FOR LOVE

MANNERS MAKETH THE MAN

THE THEATRE OF LOVE

TACKLE THE KEY ISSUE

KISS CHASE

THE HIGHWAY TO LOVE

SURPRISE PARTY—FOR TWO

YOU, THE SUPERMODEL

GETTING IT ON...

ONE OF life's most enhancing gifts, great sex matters—whether it's lingering, leisurely lovemaking with a life partner, or a delicious, daring exploration with a new lover, a satisfying session nourishes you and your relationship. Great sex makes you feel desirable and loved, revitalized and energetic. And although being mistress of the erotic arts is something of a modern myth, the art of lovemaking can really be quite simple. Your sexual power and energy is alive and well in you, the lover. You don't need permission to turn it (and him) on. Remember that, as a woman, you are a dynamic, sensual being who can offer your lover the gift of great sex any time you choose.

The secret of pleasing your partner is to enjoy yourself sexually. Many men find it a challenge having to take responsibility for pleasing their partner sexually—his biggest turn-on is knowing that you're aroused and that you love what

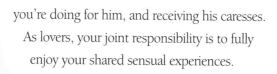

you're doing for him, and receiving his caresses. As lovers, your joint responsibility is to fully enjoy your shared sensual experiences.

In order to grow your sexuality, you need to discover what really turns you on, and make sure you share those experiences with your lover. This book gives you 50 ideas for exploring his preferences—with your own enjoyment crucial. The more you know all the different aspects of your own sexuality, the better lover you'll be, and the more you will please him! Use the book *with* him, and *on* him. It's a great feeling for him to experience you taking charge sexually—he'll love it, and adore you.

A loving relationship is one where you can both flourish sexually. Make sure you follow through with the turn-taking suggested in many tips. Recognizing that your partner will happily commit to sharing, swapping information, exploring, and experimenting in pursuit of better sex is key

to relaxing into sexual play. Many of us need to learn to receive as well as give when sharing sensual pleasure.

More erotic pleasure isn't necessarily about novelty and surprise—it comes with enriching emotional intimacy. But games and fantasy can be important too, in emphasizing a playful and creative imagination. If you can explore your private scenarios in ways that excite your own libido, your man will often be extremely responsive. Gratifying his masculine need for visual stimulation and weaving erotic fantasy into your sex life can bring you the spontaneity, freshness, and increased intensity of role-play. And, as the play leader, you will be the active agent of your own desires, too.

Just as playful sexual exploration allows you to appreciate the sensory pleasures of enjoying your own body fully, remember that your man is as sexual an object as you are, and it is a real treat for him if you regard him this way. This book shows you how to lust after your lover as the sexy one, and make sure he knows it. Show him how to affirm his sexual identity too—it can reap rewards for you both. As you work through the tips, look at him with delight and treat him like a fantastic lover.

Good sex is not all about the hot and heavy—take frequent opportunities each day outside the bedroom to express the sensual and sexy woman you are. Greet him, touch him, hug him, and listen to him. And during sex, concentrate on connecting with him, rather than going all-out for an orgasm. It's not the top priority in truly great sex— the most important sex advice you'll ever get is that orgasms tend to look after themselves if you are concentrating on pure enjoyment.

So read on for inspiration on how to really enjoy yourself in bed and you'll soon be having the best sex you've ever had with your partner. Turn the page to discover new positions, tantalizing techniques, and delectable pleasures, in the form of…

50 WAYS TO PLEASE YOUR LOVER

"MAKE YOUR MAN YOUR WILLING SLAVE... HE'LL LOVE IT, AND ADORE YOU"

1 ◇ Just Say "Yes" "yes" "yes" "yes"

A CAREFREE *way to spend time and an exercise session rolled into one—what's not to love about truly* GREAT SEX? *Give your* SEX LIFE *the commitment it deserves—and, if you're* HAPPY *with it, agree that you'll never say no for a set period of time. Not only will you reap the advantages of a more relaxed attitude,* SEX *will improve. A simple* "YES" *is a gift—it shows you intend to be* RECEPTIVE *to your partner's* SEXUAL INTEREST *and* DESIRE *for you. Of course, it's a two-way thing. When your lover affirms his* COMMITMENT *to you, you can become more spontaneous, affectionate, and willing to take the risk of initiating* SEX *without fear of rebuff.*

HERE'S THE AGREEMENT: *whoever makes an approach, the other person will always find a way to respond positively. Bypassing lack of energy, distractions, or the frustrations of a bad day, what you do is agree that neither of you will ignore or cold-shoulder the other—and this book offers over*

50 POSSIBILITIES TO TAKE THINGS FURTHER.

MANY couples believe that SEX should be spontaneous, and that scheduling SEX is a passion-killer. The fact is, though, that not timetabling it into your busy lives leads to less SEX!

So schedule SEX—because planning allows you both to make an effort preparing for a special night, and signals that your relationship is more important than anything that might come up at work just as you're leaving. And it heightens his sense of anticipation; let him know exactly what's on the menu with SEXy texts or messages.

3 ◇ S̶TEXTUAL HEALING

A SEXY phone call is the ultimate in safe sex—so let yourself go. Choose RAUNCHY, HEARTFELT, or WITTY wordplay—explore a FANTASY, describing what you plan to do to each other, or you may want to CARESS YOUR OWN BODY as if your partner were touching you. Describe your DESIRE and SENSATIONS to your partner. Or, focus on him, leading him through one of his favorite scenarios... he may want to STIMULATE HIMSELF (if he can't wait).

GIVE YOUR GUY A TREAT: *tie his hands up*, so he doesn't have to do anything. Offer your lover *a position of his choice*; to be *sitting or standing with his hands tied up*, or whether he'd like to be *tied spread-eagled* to the bed, totally at your mercy. If you *blindfold* him, too, it will focus his experience of being utterly in your loving, gentle hands. Start with a *slow, light touch*, maybe *using a feather*. Give his whole body attention, *using long strokes* to *sweep up* from his pelvis though his torso and arms, or down his thighs to his feet. After *caressing* his toes, neck, and chest, move in towards his genitals. *Caress* his lower belly, his groin along the angle of his legs, and *gently tease* his pubic hair. *Explore* his inner thighs and scrotal area and behind it the sensitive perineum, *teasing gently* as you circle round. Now repeat with your tongue—later, you can *untie him* so he can return the favor...

5 ◆ MANNERS MAKETH THE MAN —*Horny*

AGREE *to do whatever your partner wants in bed, on the understanding that he'll return the favor for an equivalent length of time. This agreement gives him permission to think about, and ask, for what he would* ENJOY *most, without having to compromise* HIS DESIRES. *It's a great technique to use on men who find it hard to talk—or know what they want. You're giving him the key to* UNLOCK HIS OWN DESIRES.

To start, AGREE *that for a four-hour block on the weekend your man will be responsible for deciding what you'll both be doing, and you will go along with* HIS WISHES, *unless there's anything you absolutely cannot bear doing! In that case, make it clear that you'll consider alternative suggestions—let him make them. What he wants is a willing playmate, and this can be* PLEASURABLE *even where it's a non-sexual activity that he wants you to share with him.*

 NEXT DAY, IT'S YOUR TURN TO FOLLOW YOUR FANCY.

As a sneaky but oh-so-hot tease, during lovemaking avoid intercourse and opt for outercourse—rubbing your genitals against different parts of each other's bodies. Slip his penis between your breasts, buttocks, thighs, legs, and toes. Avoiding intercourse is an ideal way to keep you both inventive about lovemaking!

7 ◆ SENSUAL MASSAGE

THE KEY to a DELICIOUSLY sensual massage is to recognize that it is a SENSUAL PLEASURE to be INDULGED in for its own sake, rather than a prelude to sex. Sensual massage focuses on energizing the whole body—VERY S L O W L Y—using a variety of strokes.

* START *with your partner lying on their front. Use oil (or talcum powder if you want to keep oil away from your bedding), and begin with* long, firm strokes *from the lower back up to the shoulders—use one hand on each side of his spine. Then* knead and massage *around the shoulder blades, and along the area from neck to shoulders. Let your partner* guide you *as to how much pressure they want. And once he has* relaxed *—usually after around 20 minutes—turn him over and ask him to* close his eyes ...

* NOW explore *your lover's body with* different touches. *Pay particular attention to areas you usually ignore—*massage *his chest and abdomen, before* brushing *his genitals and* lengthening the strokes *up his abdomen and chest to connect his genitals with the rest of his body.*

WHY LINGERIE MATTERS ◇ 8

MOST women love the feel of SILK and SATIN.
And if you feel as GLAMOROUS and drop-dead
GORGEOUS as a screen star, you'll probably act that
way too. Men are visual creatures and very few are not
aroused by GORGEOUS SEXY UNDERWEAR,
and some love those CLICHED CORSETS or
FLIMSY NYLON NUMBERS. Go for what you
like, though, and dress to show off
your assets. Quality LINGERIE
can also help you let go
of needless body anxieties
and boost your confidence
—as well as your bust.

◇ B_UMP 'N' G R I N D

F_{OR} A missionary style technique that's reputed to increase your chances of SIMULTANEOUS ORGASM MIGHTILY, try this B_UMP AND G R I N D routine. Called COITAL ALIGNMENT TECHNIQUE, the key is to line your genitals up so that you get maximum pressure from your clitoris down to the vagina.

* When your man is on top, ask him to WIGGLE UP a bit more, so the base of his penis is PRESSING on your clitoris and the tip is barely inside you. WRAP your legs around his and TILT your pelvis while he bears down, letting him SLIDE IN to you more.
* Forget the old missionary THRUSTING style—ROCK your pelvises together with just enough FRICTION to be extremely arousing—he'll take longer to come and you'll get there more quickly.

HAVE FUN . . .

20

For some people, words can be distracting during lovemaking and may add to uncertainty of whether they are pleasing their partner. Banish doubts and affirm mutual pleasure with the **"YES, NO, MAYBE, PLEASE"** game. It's a way of communicating what you enjoy simply to your lover—so he can "travel" your body to reach your ultimate destination with roadmap-clear directions. When your partner does something you like, just say **"YES."** To stop it, a simple **"NO"** will suffice. When you say **"MAYBE,"** your partner can try out different ways of doing the same thing—varying his pressure, touch, and pace. If you're still giving him the **"MAYBE"** feedback, he will need to move on to trying other ways of turning you on. Now take turns using the game, but keep to the four words.

11 ◆ POLE-TO-POLE DESIRE

WOULD YOUR LOVER CROSS OCEANS FOR YOU?
Try a TOUCH OF RETRO-STYLE POLE-DANCING and
he'll dive right in. Get inspired watching video clips
of burlesque queen Dita von Teese or 30s movie
goddesses to find ideas for YOUR OWN SIREN'S
STRIPTEASE. Treat yourself to a pure silk robe, bra, and
panties, and SHIMMY YOUR WAY through a sultry Wartime number.
TANTALIZE HIM. Keep your distance and allow him to GAZE AT
YOUR GYRATING BODY—or use his body as the pole. TEASE HIM by
using your breath to CARESS HIS PUBIC MOUND, and PLAYING
AROUND HIS NIPPLES, throat, lips, and FOREHEAD. He can look but
not touch—a sure way to whet his appetite.

TO REACH ORGASM, *most people tense the muscles, especially around the thighs and pelvis, but muscular tension can block energy flow through your body, shortening your orgasm or limiting it to the genital area. This technique allows your peak to spread through your whole body,* **LEADING TO ENDURING BLISS.** *When you are very aroused, sink into a state of deep relaxation, breathing deeply yet slowly. To deepen your orgasm, consciously relax your body, rather than increasing muscle tension, as you usually do when your arousal is building. If you can't reach orgasm without tensing your buttocks and thighs, try to let one or two contractions occur in your usual way, and then stop making any further effort. Let the orgasm sweep through your body.*

SURRENDER TO THE PLEASURE!

23

13 ⬦ BE A MOVIE ★ FOR A NIGHT

MEN love, just *love*, visual stimulation. And have you ever wanted to be a celebrity? Meet both your desires by starring in a very personal video. Burlesque or belly-dance classes are the new alternative to fitness classes, so why not film your inspired performance for your lover? It's for his private delectation, but if you don't want to risk any of his friends seeing your ★ turn as an erotic dancer, or you're worried clips might end up on the internet if you split up, stick to VHS, rather than a digital camera—and keep the tape yourself.

WHEN I THINK OF YOU, ♥ ◇ 14
I TOUCH. . .

Be CONFIDENT and COURAGEOUS for a night—
ABANDON YOURSELF to sexual pleasure in front of
your partner. He loves to see you SEXUALLY
STIMULATING YOURSELF in front of him—all the
way to orgasm. Touch yourself with a SENSUAL
PLEASURE and explore your own body as if you
were your own lover. Don't try too hard—TAKE
YOUR TIME AND ENJOY. And remember, he can
use those same tried-and-tested techniques to
great effect later; that's ample incentive to
overcome your shyness.

15 ◆ DELICIOUS DETAILS

GOOD COMMUNICATION *is vital to great sex. Tell your lover exactly what you find attractive and what you love about his lovemaking. Your partner is not a mind reader. You may be surprised to discover that your man doesn't always feel confident about what he's doing in bed. He can't know exactly what you're experiencing and he sometimes can't read your body language in order to know how excited you are—or occasionally if you're excited at all. And if you don't make any noise when you orgasm, how is he to find out except by asking? So to put him out of his misery, and put paid to the tentative post-coital query,*

"HOW WAS IT FOR YOU?,"

you need to tell him—in great detail.

ORAL PLAY is a deeply erotic experience. Many couples consider it even more intimate than intercourse. Exploring each other's LIPS and TONGUES is evidence of YOUR JUICY CONNECTION—and yes, SHARING THE BODY FLUIDS of your lover is particularly intimate. KISS his forehead, brow, earlobes, cheeks, or chin. Try LICKING, SUCKING, or NIBBLING parts of his face and neck. Does he like BLOWING, SUCKING, OR LICKING? Don't forget NOSE-RUBBING and BUTTERFLY KISSES using your eyelashes. Sharing taste sensations can be great fun with TONGUE PLAY. Share some chocolate, liqueur, or crushed berries. Let your KISSES be subtle, sensual, and varied.

Kiss Kiss Kiss Kiss Kiss Kiss

17 ◇ TACKLE THE KEY ISSUE

*S*PEND A *session focusing on his genitals—you know he loves it. You can always find out more about his likes and dislikes. Discover what quality of* **TOUCH** *and* **PRESSURE** *drives him crazy. Too many women assume that a man is easy to satisfy because his erections come easily, but refining your techniques for penile stimulation will make him feel cared for and fully satisfied. Use a variety of moves—firm pressure, or the lightest touch, with* **FLICKS, LICKS, TICKLES.**

See if he enjoys **SCRATCHING**, ꜱǫᴜᴇᴇᴢɪɴɢ, *using gentle circling massage movements. Don't forget the underside and base of his penis, his scrotum, and the area towards his anus. Pressure in the perineum can feel great while you play with the rest of his tackle.*

If you or your lover hankers after SPICE and NOVELTY, act on it. What adventure would you like to explore? Choose a scenario based on discussions with your man—then seize the moment. Why not show him a side of yourself that he doesn't yet know? Inhabit your secret sexual persona—DRESS UP, RUB YOUR BODY ON HIS WHILE FULLY CLOTHED, or, when you feel overwhelmed by lust, MAKE A GRAB FOR HIM IN A SEMI-PUBLIC PLACE. Remember that staying partially dressed or keeping on all your underwear while you arouse each other can be a great appetizer.

19 ◆ VALLEY GIRL (and BOY)

"VALLEY" STYLE ORGASMS are like the countryside, full of PEAKS and VALLEYS rather than a single climax. To go for valley orgasms, STRENGTHEN your pelvic floor muscles with Kegel exercises—something you can diligently practice daily without letting your man know. When they're TONED UP, you can surprise him with a MUSCULAR CLENCH of his penis—LOOK, NO HANDS! And once you've built great muscle tone you can E X T E N D your orgasm into the VALLEY by RHYTHMICALLY SQUEEZING your pelvic floor muscles—to intensify your contractions, he can do the same, SQUEEZING his pelvic muscles, giving you both even more pleasure . . .

Use an Erotic Emporium ◇ 20

Obvious as it sounds, a good sex shop CAN REALLY HELP YOUR LOVE LIFE. Order up a wide selection of catalogues, and check them out together. Apart from WHAT TAKES YOUR FANCY in the way of merchandise, there's nothing quite like trying on outfits in the store to remind your lover what he truly wants. Classy chains include *Myla* and *Agent Provocateur*, or independent sex shops such as *Good Vibrations* (SAN FRANCISCO) stock soft porn videos made by women, if you like that sort of thing. Make an evening of visiting several sex shops—AND HAVE FUN. Invite your man to choose WHATEVER TAKES HIS FANCY; whether it's clothes, toys, or erotic aids to gaze upon...

21 ❖ USE HIS BODY AS A CANVAS FOR YOUR EROTIC ARTISTRY

SOME women assume that men don't need much SEXUAL STIMULATION–in fact, our partners could often do with a lot more touching and more variety to boost their erections. So find out how your lover responds to every SENSUAL STIMULATION–is he sensitive to smell, taste, and sound as well as touch and what he's seeing? Use his whole body as the canvas for your SENSUAL EXPERIMENTATION and try to fit as many SENSATIONS as you can into your lovemaking session, without overstimulating him into a quick orgasm. Start with LOW, WARM-COLORED LIGHTING, GENTLE MUSIC, and SCENTED CANDLES to ramp up the SEXY MOOD, then tease him

with SLOW STROKES that cover every inch of him. Try MOIST foods, talcum powder, oils, or LUBRICANTS to vary the texture of skin on skin. Finally, TANTALIZE HIM with a variety of fabrics and feathers to STROKE, WRAP, and BRUSH his skin. You'll drive him wild!

22 ◆ You, The SUPERmodel

*T*HIS SEDUCTIVE *strategy is a simple joy for most women—and a chance to make the most of the* LOVELY LINGERIE *and* DRESSES *you like to show off. Time to wear them for the most special occasion of all—in the privacy of your own home, and for a particularly appreciative audience—your lover. Pick your favorite pieces: clothes that make you feel beautiful, powerful, and sexy, or that reveal any of your secret alter egos. Whether your style is* DESIGNER, GIRLY, SHINY, *or* SEE-THROUGH, *your preferred fabrics* SILK, SATIN, LEATHER, *or* RUBBER, *your colors* PEARL, BLACK, *or* PINK, *your underwear* CORSETS *and* SUSPENDERS, *or* NEGLIGIBLE NEGLIGEES, *embrace your unique style and parade with pride.*

THE LOVERS' DANCE ◇ 23

THE ORIGINS OF erotic dance are buried in mystery—but the tradition of women using dance as seduction is ancient. From Salome to Mata Hari, women worldwide know that an erotic shimmy can enthrall a lover. For your own dance, start by decorating your bedroom beforehand—drapes, flowers, and even scented air will set the scene. Pick an outfit that brings out the performer in you, and choose a long-ish piece of music that moves you—you need to become absorbed and lose your inhibitions. As you move, remember that understatement can be more fascinating; start with subtle, sinuous movements of your hips and torso. Once you feel more adventurous, let the music move your body. Explore different moods toward your partner; try being refined, raunchy, or playful. And invite your lover to join the dance.

24 ◆ Size Matters

If your man is worried about being too small, go on top and lean back for MAXIMUM STIMULATION. He might not know that only a few women can orgasm with intercourse alone, and that giving you MAXIMUM ATTENTION with his mouth or hands, or from more bump and grind while he's inside you, will make him a GREAT lover. He could also make you come before even entering you—many women love oral sex for their first orgasm. It's good manners for him to let you come first and then he can feel GREAT about his PROWESS as a lover and go for his own pleasure.

BE A VIRGIN FOR A NIGHT—*many men love it. Rekindling the first fumblings reminds the average guy of his early, highly-charged experiences. What sort of virgin turns him on? Will you be a* COY MAID, *with whom he must be delicately considerate and gentle? Or are you an* INNOCENT WOMAN *who hasn't yet discovered her love of sex, whom your lover awakens with his passion and expertise? Are you and your swain a* GAWKY AND INEXPERIENCED COUPLE, *who spend a long night tentatively touching without going the whole way?*

Pick an outfit to suit the scenario: HEAVY, FUNCTIONAL UNDERWEAR, ROLL-NECKED TOPS *that are difficult to get off,* PLEATED SKIRTS *with* WHITE COTTON KNICKERS. *Get into the mood with heavy petting—caress, stroke, and kiss through your clothes as you work out how to take them off... before gazing in awe at each other's body. Let him take his time studying the art of oral sex. There's no rush to get onto the next stage.*

26 ◆ MAKE THE FIRST MOVE

YES, YOU! Why does he always have to approach you? Men commonly complain they have to initiate sex all the time, which can become a burden. But if you initiate sex, your lover will feel affirmed. Take TIME TO TOUCH HIM in a sexual way. Lay your claim to his body with A CONFIDENT HAND THAT IS SURE OF A POSITIVE RESPONSE; rub yourself against him; pressing your body against his in ways that make your intent clear. LET HIM KNOW HOW MUCH YOU WANT AND DESIRE HIM.

Confident men like older women because they are confident, sassy, and independent. They know who they are and what they want. And guys love it when you take on the role of a SEXY, self-assured woman who can initiate them into the realms of the EROTIC arts. Experience the value of your SEXUAL POWER and inhabit that role for one night. Make it your job to teach him everything you know—including your personal HOT TIPS. Maybe he's the virgin, wanting to be initiated at your altar. Use your wealth of experience and reap the rewards of this

INTIMATE mentoring process.

Coach him and inspire him!

28 ◆ COMPLY WITH YOUR ORDERS . . .

SUBMISSION *is a perennial staple of many private fantasies. Many of us are uncomfortable with acknowledging the titillation that* fantasies *of being* sexually dominated *can provide, but remember that confident couples treat* fantasy *as* fantasy, *knowing where the limits are.*

Agree the outfit; is it a laced bodice, a business suit, or a dress that would be satisfying to rip off? Or is it more the physical sensations of wrestling and pressing your bodies together with vigorous sex that excites you? But submission *is only fun if you truly consent—so agree a safe word to stop the scenario in advance. Avoid* "stop" *or* "no" *since you may well be shrieking this at full throttle—use a neutral word, such as* "berry." *And use an abundant dose of lubricant to make sure that rough play doesn't actually hurt.*

Taking Too L o n g ? ◆ 29

If your man takes ages to come, he's not really getting enough of the right kind of STIMULATION. He might also be feeling anxious about sex and need to learn to receive.

* Just concentrate on CARESSING his whole body, focusing on whatever AROUSES HIM. Your job is to encourage him to SURRENDER TO PLEASURE. Enjoy exploring all the different ways you can TURN HIM ON—this is a gourmet experience for him to enjoy NEW and SUBTLE SEXUAL FLAVORS.

* Round off your WHOLE BODY MASSAGE with a good hand job—keep CHANGING YOUR STYLE AND PACE to give him as much VARIETY as you can come up with. Whatever you do—don't rush him!

30 ◆ APPETITE FOR LOVE

Is YOUR lover as delicious as chocolate or your favorite TREAT? Show him exactly how much you fancy him by making him your very own banquet for one. For your most delectable dish, cover his body with mouthwatering food and decorate him with moreish treats, strategically positioned over his erogenous zones. Try SUGGESTIVELY-SHAPED FRUITS, CHOCOLATE MOUSSE, VANILLA CREAM, TRUFFLES or PRALINES, and FRESH BERRIES.

*L*UBRICATION *is always good. Using it is not a sign that what's happening isn't arousing enough —* LUBRICATION *improves* SENSATION, *turning just* FRICTION *into a* PLEASURABLE GLIDE.

You can choose your LUBE *from a sex shop or local pharmacy, but look too in your kitchen. Any kind of quality* OIL *can be pressed into action: olive oil is* RICH *and* CREAMY *and feels great but tends to ruin your sheets, so make sure you're not laying on anything you mind ruining!*

VIBRATORS *can be a girl's best friend, giving that extra* BURST OF STIMULATION *if you're flagging. Some women swear by* THE RAMPANT RABBIT, *while others prefer an* EXTERNAL BUZZ *on the clitoris.* THE MAGIC WAND *delivers* MAXIMUM STIMULATION, *and your man might enjoy this applied to his perineum for that* EXTRA THRILL…

32 ◆ A PRIVATE TOUR OF THE LADY GARDEN . . .

USUALLY when he's up-close to your sex, your lover feels he has to take action—but give him a thrill by just letting him gaze and admire for five minutes or so. By doing so, you're offering him a chance to satisfy his fascination, his voyeurism, and his sheer delight in your intimate beauty. Lie back naked and close your eyes—he can share his thoughts with you afterward, telling you how much he enjoyed getting to know the source of much of his sexual pleasure more intimately....

THE THEATRE OF LOVE ◇ 33

THE MOST **POWERFUL** EROTIC
TOOL of all, enlist your
IMAGINATION to develop your
mutual satisfaction using the power
of SEXUAL FANTASY. A GOOD FANTASY is a
piece of theatre that you create during the performance. But
once the curtain comes down, it's over. So lose the shyness and
fix a date with your lover to SHARE YOUR FANTASIES; RECALL
OLD FANTASIES, SEXUAL MEMORIES, and EROTIC DREAMS
and use the time to discover more about each other's EROTIC
TURN-ONS. If you don't have any favorite fantasies, make one
up on the spot and take turns to develop the plot together.

Find out what sort of ENVIRONMENT turns your partner on. Is he a CLOSET NATURIST who likes to MAKE LOVE IN THE WOODS or WHILE FROLICKING IN THE OCEAN? Is he excited by the thrill of potential discovery, PREFERRING A PASSIONATE *quickie* IN AN ALLEYWAY OFF A BUSY THOROUGHFARE, or IN A PRIVATE CUBICLE AT A RESTAURANT where the waiter might turn up at any time?

ONLY ONE WAY TO FIND OUT...

LOCATION, LOCATION, LOCATION

Switch Lovers' Roles ◆ 35

LOVERS express complementary sexual energies at different times—sometimes one partner takes on the passionate, active, masculine energy of the pursuer, while the other is caring, receptive, and feminine. Many people enjoy taking on the opposite of their usual role, or take turns exploring both active and passive roles during lovemaking. For instance, where your man is habitually caring and considerate, it may be great fun to access chest-beating macho behavior where sex is about conquest. He'll need permission to get into role, and you can help him by playing whatever typically ladylike role you would enjoy as his counterpoint—maybe a repressed Victorian about to be overwhelmed by his primal sexual energy, or a helpless victim, or a coquette. As the reverse, he can play the coy young woman, concealing his penis between his thighs. If you take over his sexual style, making love as if he were a woman can be interesting for you both.

36 ◆ Bathed in Love

Run a herb-scented, oily bath and light the bathroom with the soft glow of candles. Undress your man and let him slide in. Using a HUGE SOFT SPONGE, wash him as carefully as if he were your precious child, STROKING each limb with tenderness. Soap him SLOWLY and THOROUGHLY. After his bath, wrap him in a FLUFFY TOWEL and PAT HIM DRY all over. Then offer him a RUB DOWN with TALCUM POWDER. As a preparation for sex, this is TRULY MELLOW and makes your lover feel cared for in the most SOOTHING, GENTLE way—but it can be even more intimate if you just lie together, saving further action for another time.

48

DOES your man enjoy a bit of SPANKING? How do you feel about administering a bit of CORPORAL PUNISHMENT? If you both like the idea, start by testing his limits for pain—he may find the idea a TURN-ON but not actually enjoy the experience. If your lover was punished at school, the typical scenario may call for a short skirt and school blazer. Or try dominatrix staging—improvise a simple scenario where you strip your man and TIE HIM TO THE BED OR A CHAIR. Arouse him with your CARESSES—you're in total control here, so you may want TO BIND HIS HANDS as well. Once he's excited, try a little PUNISHMENT. Then CARESS his buttocks and the rest of his body, to create the TINGLING PLEASURE the PAIN-PLEASURE combination arouses.

38 ◆ UNLEASH THE INNER STYLIST

*H*AND *your lover the scissors for a spot of* "intimate" HAIRDRESSING. *Once you have discussed the design, invite him to shave your pubic hair into* a ♥, a ★, *or any other shape you would both enjoy. Some men like* a rectangular landing strip, *an* ↑, *or their* initials — *or remove all the hair. You can have fun, too, with* temporary tattoos *or henna tattooing to paint* serpents, dragons, butterflies, *and* orchid tendrils *diving towards your labia, or climbing up towards your navel. Latest fashions also include* zebra-skin *and* leopard-skin *designs, or the* "Chaplin moustache" *for him.*

♥ ♥ ♥ ♥ ♥ ♥ ♥ ♥

WORD-OF-MOUTH ♦

THE ART of good fellatio is to let your lover know how much you enjoy it—that way he can relax and receive. And if you're not sure, ask him—he's bound to let you know just how much he appreciates it. Oral sex is also often a GREAT VISUAL TURN-ON, so he may want to prop himself up on pillows in order to get a good view. Stay on top, move your head freely, and take your time. For variety, treat his genitals as an ICE CREAM, and maybe add CUSTARD, CREAM, or CHOCOLATE SAUCE. As well as LICKING, KISSING, SUCKING, and SQUEEZING, try gently FLICKING and holding different parts of him. Don't forget his scrotum and perineum—very lightly, run your nails lightly towards his perineum while your tongue dances around his shaft. You'll know he's getting close to orgasm when his breathing becomes shorter gasps. Never feel you need to do a "deep throat," or agonize over whether you should swallow.

40 ❖ FLIRTING WITH*ongs* FETISHISM

IF YOUR MAN is typically out in the CUT AND THRUST of the corporate world, or has minions running round after him, he may enjoy a bit of role reversal. If you think he secretly longs for someone else to take charge, call in your inner DOMINATRIX for the night. Don your most teetering HEELS, and dress up in LEATHER, LATEX, THONGS, BUCKLES, or FUR. Make sure dungeon equipment such as BUCKLES, HANDCUFFS, LEATHER TIES, a BLIND-FOLD or perhaps a PADDLE, WHIP, or CANE is to hand.

Domination isn't really about the bondage gear and posing, it's about you taking charge of your lover. You'll discover that you can play him LIKE AN INSTRUMENT.

FAST and FURIOUS,
or SLOW and MOODY,
BUILDING HIM UP and
LETTING HIM DOWN just
as you like, and bringing him to a climax when you want.
Dominating him means being selfish, so please yourself
along the way—use his body to arouse yourself, and his
pleasure to increase your own. After all, he's your
willing SEXUAL SLAVE.

HE'LL LOVE IT, AND ADORE YOU.

41 ◆ THE FINAL FRONTIER

MOST couples try anal sex at least once, although the figures are not high for continuing. Some couples love it, though, and if you're keen, remember that the anus is more of a pouch than the vagina, and very shallow penetration stimulates the sensitive anal area. But the skin here is delicate, so use lots of lubrication for the first time – he should keep it very slow and gentle till you find out what feels good for you. Many men love stimulation of their anus and the perineum, the area between their scrotum and anus. This can be a great turn-on on its own or during intercourse. Devoting a session to exploring the erotic potential of the anus can be a great gift to your lover. Maybe he's the one who likes to be penetrated, rather than you. There are plenty of sex toys available to try on him, whether handheld or strap-on.

(For good hygiene, your partner should use a condom for anal penetration.)

SOMEWHERE in every man's unconscious mind—or maybe even his conscious mind— your BREASTS are forever associated with the primal delights of breastfeeding, when his mother was his whole soft, loving world. The thought of being CRADLED AT YOUR BREASTS can give your lover a deeply soothing sense of being loved. Get in touch with your nurturing instincts and give your man the experience of unconditional love by CRADLING HIM IN YOUR ARMS. Allow him to relax and let go into your loving care. Try and stay in a non-sexual maternal role if possible, because maybe it's best not to make this the prelude to a hot and heavy session—even if he is sucking your BREASTS and turning you on. It could be confusing for you both. And if you're feeling envious—remember it can be tough having to act grown up all the time. In return, allow yourself to TAKE REFUGE IN HIS ARMS TOO.

43 ◇ Filling The Eye With Beauty

Many people are used to disappearing inside their heads and running into a predictable fantasy in order to reach orgasm when self-pleasuring. Some people even keep this up when they're making love—not ideal for great sex because true lovemaking requires deep connection. Boost your erotic togetherness by pleasuring yourselves while maintaining eye contact throughout—most couples find it incredibly exciting. You'll get the visual pleasure of seeing your lover in sexual abandon, as well as his response to yours.

TANTRIC TITILLATION ◇

*T*HE *most effective way to explore tantric techniques is to use breathing and visualization to take your focus away from your genital sensations.*

* *W*hile your partner is CARESSING *your body and* STIMULATING *you, focus on encouraging the* SENSATIONS *to spread out and* ENLIVEN *your whole body. Spend some time doing this—it's a different experience to the more traditional focus on the* RACE TO ORGASM.

* *U*se your breath to create a physical connection between the two of you. *Imagine that you're drawing in your partner's* EROTIC ENERGY *as you inhale his out-breath; he can do the same. Doing this for a few minutes creates a* HEADY FEELING *of hypoxia (produced by breathing in carbon dioxide)—it's part of the* ECSTASY *tantric* LOVEMAKING *can induce.*

* *A*fter orgasm, bathe in BLISS *together.*

45 ◇ Play The Fame Game

Many people FANTASIZE about sex with someone famous. Just for him, take on the stage persona of his favorite celebrity and act out scenes from their greatest films. Whether you want to play Scarlett O'Hara in *Gone with the Wind*, or a 30s screen goddess in a *film noir*, it's your mutual choice. Use the movie's plot as the storyboard for your PRIVATE FANTASY. Then create your own star-studded story of an intense romance in which you are both gorgeous, sexy, and magnetically attracted to each other. Bask in this CORNUCOPIA of your FANTASY LIFE for one evening—and when you wake, you'll be a little bit more aware that your relationship is the fount of your positive feelings and values.

*M*OST *men get a huge ego boost by* having a sexy woman on their arm. *If you suspect your lover gets a thrill out of* showing you off, *find out what sort of venue he wants to parade you at. It may be just a trip to his local bar or his sports club, or even the work party. Ask him what he wants you to wear—maybe a low-cut dress that* spellbinds other guys *with a glimpse of your* lovely breasts, *or tight jeans that reveal* a pert bottom *and* endless legs. *He might prefer you to wear a modest outfit that conceals your best lingerie, or he may find it enormously sexy if you* leave lingerie out altogether *—he can remind himself that you're knickerless visually or with his hand at various points throughout the evening. Some men love it if you* "ACCIDENTALLY" forget your panties *at a dull work social or at a dreaded family event.*

47 ◆ LAP DANCING

CRAWL ALONG towards your man, eyeing his erection.
When he's SITTING COMFORTABLY, and you're
feeling turned on, sit on his lap with his penis inside
you. Spend as much time KISSING and LOOKING at
each other the whole time—which many couples find
DEEPLY INTIMATE. As your hands are free
to CARESS his torso and back, your
EROTIC HUNGER will intensify. Just
keep rolling and grinding your
pelvises, keeping your
EXCITEMENT UP.

Help Him Last Longer ◇ 48

As MANY guys have inadvertently trained themselves to come quickly through years of masturbation, they can be ashamed when they come in minutes, if not seconds. If your man comes too rapidly for either of your tastes, you can help him to CONTROL HIS AROUSAL. PLEASURE YOUR PARTNER right to the edge of your orgasm, then STOP and just hold him. Before his erection completely subsides (don't let him get anxious about whether it comes back), START STIMULATING HIM AGAIN. See how many times he can approach the edge of orgasm, then retreat. Over time, this technique gives him the confidence in his ability to master his sexual control switch.

49 ◆ Use HIM Up, Wear HIM Out

Your lover will probably enjoy being an instrument for your SEXUAL PLEASURE. *With minimal consideration for him, let him experience what it's like being at the receiving end of a* VORACIOUS SEXUAL APPETITE *where you use his body to stimulate yourself.* Rub *your pubic area against his thighs and* press *whichever parts of your body you want* licked *or* sucked *into his mouth. Use his penis for your pleasure;* rub *it against your thighs, labia, or clitoris in just the way that turns you on. It's up to you what quality of* pressure *you want and how long for. Just go for it! Your man will probably be in heaven witnessing you lustily* making use of *his body.*

During sex, climb on top so that you can control the speed, angle, *and depth that give you* MAXIMUM STIMULATION, *whether it's* playing *at the entrance to your vagina, or the* deep penetration *at an angle that* STIMULATES *your G-spot. Tell him how you want him to* shift position *to* UP YOUR PLEASURE, *or what you want him to do with his hands and mouth. Order him about!*

The Fast and Furious Sex ◆ 50

DELIGHT your man by **seizing the moment**, and taking his trousers down when you have only five minutes to spare, or even when you're in a semi-public place. The **urgency of your need** will give your partner a huge frisson—and the location may awaken the exhibitionist in you. QUICKIES sex can be fine if you frequently enjoy quality sex and are easily orgasmic, otherwise they could leave you sore or frustrated. Try stimulating yourself just beforehand, so that you're already aroused and **physically ready for it!**